Skunk Wants to Play

Lalie Harcourt & Ricki Wortzman

Illustrated by June Bradford

gagelearning

Skunk wants to play in the park.
At the park, she finds 1 bird
and 2 squirrels.

3

"This is fun," said Skunk.

4

Skunk and her friends
want to play at the pond.
At the pond, they find 3 frogs.

"This is fun," said Skunk and her friends.

Skunk and her friends
want to play at the farm.
At the farm, they find 4 pigs.

"This is fun," said Skunk and her friends.

PLEASE
DO NOT
FEED THE
ANIMALS

Skunk and her friends
want to play at the zoo.
At the zoo, they find 5...

14

15

"This is fun," they all said.